A Bolt From The Blue

A Comedy by David Tristram

A Flying Ducks Publication

Director's Notes

CASTING:

A Bolt From The Blue offers unlimited flexibility for casting – it can be produced with as few as three actors, or with as many as you can muster, dependent on your company's strengths.

In its purest form, you'll need just two males and one female, but if you go this route make sure to cast your most experienced and competent performers, because all three roles are extremely demanding.

The play is adapted from the novel of the same name. In the minimalist version one actor plays the central character of Edward Jones, while the other two play a male narrator, a female narrator, plus every other character in the story.

However, if you think it would be better to spread the load and involve more people, you have the option to replace any number of the other character parts with different actors, and of course any amount of doubling within that is acceptable. You'd then also have the further option, if you wished, to consolidate the male and female narrators into one narrator – male or female. If you choose to use more actors than three, a few of the lines or actions in the script may no longer be applicable, or may need minor adaptation. These are marked in square brackets with an asterisk *[like this]* and common sense will dictate why these lines are no longer appropriate. Feel free to 'tweak' or omit these lines to suit your casting. Because of the various casting options, you'll find I haven't always bothered to mention formal entrances and exits in the stage notes – apart from being self-obvious most the time, it's also not relevant if the actor is already on stage and merely changing character.

Oh – and one last thing on casting – the character playing Nugent (a fairly major role) needs to be either bald (or at least sport a good bald wig) or you'll need to omit another small section of text *[also marked thus]*. This may, of course, be the same actor who plays all the male parts other than Edward, but that doesn't really matter.

THE SET:

As we have to cover a number of environments in the book, in the original production I opted for a minimalist multipurpose set. The main extravagance was a wooden climbing frame-style apparatus which I had specially constructed to represent the top of an electricity pylon. This looked especially effective when lit, and added height to the set. It was placed centrally, with a large bench-style seating device in front of it, which doubled as a settee, a garden bench, the front seat of a car, and a bed. This device also screened off the bottom of the pylon, so Edward could fall down behind it and be hidden during the dramatic opening.

Other than that, I opted for minimalism. I had a couple of other black boxes made, one either side of the stage, which variously doubled as a table, a doctor's desk, hospital reception desk, informal podiums and seats for the narrators, and so on. Being black and anonymous, it made it easier to transform from one setting to another quickly, with just with the addition of a few simple props, such as a pillow, telephone, or vase of flowers.

SPECIAL EFFECTS:

One thing you might curse me for is this rather casual stage note:

Sarah collapses back onto the bench. Suddenly, her stomach begins swelling like a gigantic inflating balloon. Edward is horrified but helpless.

Yes, I know - easier said than done, but at least I do always test the practicality of my plays first with a low budget production of my own. Your technical team will have great fun with this. We tried a few theories before we came across a low-tech but reliable answer. As Sarah sits down on the bench, our stage manager opened a little trap door in the upright behind her back and grabbed a tube which was hidden inside Sarah's clothing. The tube was taped to a giant balloon lining her abdomen, between two layers of stretchy fabric. Under cover of the dramatic music, the stage manager attached the tube to a soda stream refill canister (I think we got ours from Tesco), pressed the button and – bingo – she started inflating.

We even got cocky and wanted to time the bang to the last note of the music. No problem. The balloon was a big one, and unlikely to burst before we wanted it to, so a subtle prick with a pin from Edward as he finally moved forward to help her did the trick. As I say – low tech, but it worked, every night, and amazed the crowds.

MUSIC:

One last thought about music. I used a lot in my production – not just to link scenes but also to underpin key moments by playing it subtly under speeches – scary, romantic, eerie, magical - it adds so much atmosphere to use music in this cinematic way, and with modern technology making precision timing easy it's well worth taking time to source and create your soundtrack carefully and thereby enhance the whole audio-visual experience. For many societies, clever lighting can be too expensive and impractical – but sound needn't be.

Anyway, that's enough from me. I'll leave the rest to your fertile imagination.

PERFORMING LICENCES

Rights of performance by Amateurs and Professionals are controlled by Samuel French Limited, 52, Fitzroy Street, London W1T 5JR.

Samuel French, or their authorized agents, issue licences on payment of a fee.

It is an infringement of the Copyright to give any performance or public reading of this play before the fee has been paid and the licence issued.

The publication of this play does not imply that it is necessarily available for performance by Amateurs or Professionals, either in the British Isles or Overseas.

Amateurs and Professionals considering a production are strongly advised, in their own interests, to apply to Samuel French, or their overseas agents, for consent before starting rehearsals or booking a theatre or hall.

VIDEO RECORDING OF AMATEUR PRODUCTIONS

Please note that the copyright laws governing video recording are extremely complex and that it should not be assumed that any play may be video recorded for whatever purpose without first obtaining the permission of the appropriate agents. The fact that a play is published does not indicate that video rights are available or that Samuel French control such rights.

For more information on Flying Ducks, check the web site.

www.flyingducks.biz

ISBN: 1-900997-07-X
978 -1-900997-07-2

A Flying Ducks Publication

A Bolt From The Blue

A play by David Tristram

Act One

Powerful music emphasizes the drama of a huge lightning storm. Edward Jones, drenched and despairing, has climbed to the top of an electricity pylon. He turns to the sky, screaming "Help me! Please, help me!" Suddenly, there's an almighty crack of thunder and an explosive lightning bolt strikes, lighting up the pylon and sending Edward plummeting down. The music hits a crescendo and ends. Calm after the storm. A spotlight fades up on the Male Narrator, who is reading a novel. He looks up.

Male Narrator: The story you're about to hear is, quite literally, incredible. It defies belief. It defies logic. It defies the fundamental laws of science and nature. And yet…

He stands.

It's the story contained in this novel – A Bolt from The Blue. And tonight, with the help of a few friends, I'm going to attempt to bring this incredible story to the stage. It won't be easy. After all, a novel can take us anywhere, anytime, it can change backdrop in the blink of an eye, employ a cast of thousands and not give two hoots for your lighting budget. A novel doesn't need understudies, rehearsals or props. A novel rarely, if ever, forgets its lines. I hate novels.

Nevertheless, our task tonight is to bring this story…to the stage. Now obviously, in order to pull it off, we'll have to cut a few corners *[so some of us will be playing more than one part]* and at times you're really going to have to use your imagination. But I hope that, in the end, you'll think it's all been worthwhile. Because the story is so very, very…incredible. In fact, the only reason that I believe it myself, is because… *(an eerie drone of music adds tension)* I was there. Yes. I actually saw it happen, with my own eyes.

Glancing at the novel.

So. Here goes.

He opens the book at the beginning and reads.

Edward Jones was eating a ham sandwich when he was struck by lightning.

An almighty thunder crack.

The details, unfortunately, are a little sketchy. Edward was the only first-hand witness. But with a little detective work, we can piece together most of the facts.

First of all, it was definitely ham. Edward always had ham on a Friday, and his wife, Mary, later confirmed that she had packed four rounds of Sainsbury's finest. We also know that the time was 1.07pm - the time that the glass on Edward's watch face melted onto the dial, encapsulating the fingers.

The only other salient fact is that, at the time of impact, Edward was suspended sixty feet in the air, strapped to an electricity pylon.

We see Edward climb up a structure behind the narrator and busy himself checking it. The Female Narrator takes up the story.

Female Narrator: Now, it was not unusual for Edward to be strapped to an electricity pylon. He spent most of his working life either up a pylon, down a pylon, or driving to another pylon. He worked for a Utilities company performing routine maintenance, and on this particular occasion, he was in the process of mending a connector which had been badly damaged during a violent storm on the previous evening. The connector had, in fact, been struck by lightning.

Edward is examining the connector curiously.

Male Narrator: Now, there's an old saying about lightning, the gist of which is that it tends not to re-visit old haunts. Just Edward's luck, then, that he was in the vicinity of a bolt which was determined to buck the trend.

Female Narrator: But there was something else. Something more bizarre. As Edward leant back to examine his lunch, perfectly trusting the integrity of the leather harness which held him high above the Shropshire countryside, he began whistling. And he did that because he was enjoying one of nature's wonders - a beautiful summer's day. The birds were singing, the butterflies were fluttering, the sheep were grazing, the sun was casting its golden glow on the cornfields. Not even a breath of wind. It seems that Edward was hit with, quite literally, a bolt from the blue.

A huge flash and bang. Edward drops from the structure behind a panel and out of sight. A farmer enters and acts out the scene.

The local farmer was the first on the scene.

Farmer: *(as if giving a statement)* Well, I 'eard this terrific bang while I was out on the tractor, and I turned just in time to see a smouldering figure plummeting from the pylon at the edge of our field.

Female Narrator: I see. And what's that, also at the edge of your field, directly under the pylon?

Farmer: Oh, that'll be an enormous mound of freshly dumped manure.

Female Narrator: The involuntary skydiver disappeared with a muted squelch.

Both sets of eyes follow the imaginary figure plummeting down. There's a suitable sound effect, and they wince.

Now there's no doubt that the manure would have helped break the fall. It's also possible that it might have had a beneficial cooling effect on Edward's charred skin. But it did nothing to encourage any would-be rescuer.

Farmer: Well, I made a few calls on my mobile - emergency services and stuff - and then I sort of cautiously circled the mound, listening for muffled cries.

Female Narrator: And then?

Farmer: And then, I waited for back-up.

Exit Farmer. Spotlight on Female Narrator.

Female Narrator: The fire brigade were the first to respond. Then the paramedics. Soon there was a small but enthusiastic crowd of spectators, who watched proceedings from a respectful distance, carefully balancing the needs of eye and nose. Last to arrive on the scene were the local First Responders, who had only found out about the emergency when they arrived home from their first-aid course.

Enter Fire Chief.

The Fire Chief took control, taking a few anxious minutes to assess the situation. It was far from straightforward.

Fire Chief: *(climbing partially up the pylon for a better view, he speaks through a megaphone)* This is one hell of a pile of shit.

Female Narrator: It was. And from sixty feet, and in total freefall, Edward's progress into the mound had been irresistible. His body had drilled a path deep into its steaming core. Winching him back through the human-shaped plughole was a non-starter. Too much suction. Besides, someone that exact shape would have had to follow him in with a rope, and then find the elbow room to attach it.

Fire Chief: Any volunteers? Thought not. *(Descending)* All right, we'll have to dig him out. *(He grabs a shovel)*

Female Narrator: A small army of dedicated professionals started nibbling round the edges of the steaming mound with shovels.

The Fire Chief eventually drags Edward's body into view.

It was a hot day. You could cut the atmosphere with a knife. No-one was seriously expecting to pull Edward from the manure alive and, as the charred and stinking body was eventually unearthed, the paramedic on standby to give mouth-to-mouth was keeping his fingers crossed that it wasn't even a close call. So you can imagine everyone's surprise when suddenly...

Edward sits bolt upright and gasps. The Fire Chief then takes up the story.

Fire Chief: His face was completely black, except for two white ovals where his glasses had been. And one of his eyebrows was missing. He looked like a startled raccoon. Or is it a negative of a raccoon? Either way, it was a raccoon with one eyebrow. Smoke was gently twirling from the spiked ends of his hair, and his left-hand was clutching a ham toasty.

Female Narrator: Then, with the assembled spectators watching in stunned silence, Edward gave a curious faint smile, hic-coughed, and passed out.

Fire Chief: Get this man into the ambulance!

Dramatic music, a wailing siren, and a blue flashing light. Edward is dragged onto the bed and urgently attended by two paramedics. It's better if the bench can be rotated round so that Edward's feet point to the audience, with a paramedic on each side.

Female Paramedic: Male Caucasian – approximately forty years old – been struck by lightning – ETA, ten minutes.
Male Paramedic: Edward? Edward can you hear me?
Female Paramedic: BP 436 over 90 and rising.
Male Paramedic: 200cc of adrenaline…
Female Paramedic: Severely tachycardic.
Male Paramedic: 500cc petrol engine…
Female Paramedic: Fairly tacky jumper.
Male Paramedic: Edward – can you feel your legs?
Female Paramedic: Systolic pressure dropping…
Male Paramedic: Can you feel anything?

Female Paramedic: 90...64...12...
Male Paramedic: Move it! We're losing him!
Female Paramedic: Get a blood match here!
Male Paramedic: He's arrested.
Female Paramedic: Stand back!
Male Paramedic: Clear!

The Female Paramedic produces two steam irons, places them on Edward's chest and shocks him.

Female Paramedic: *(grabbing the Male Paramedic's wrist)* I've got a pulse.
Male Paramedic: That's me!
Female Paramedic: 100 milligrams of hydrocortisone and one bag of creosote.
Male Paramedic: Edward?
Female Paramedic: BP 97.2FM in stereo, 909 and 693 medium wave...
Male Paramedic: What are you talking about?
Female Paramedic: I don't know.
Edward: Uggh...
Male Paramedic: Edward? Edward?

Edward slumps, lights to black.

Female Narrator: Now, there are, of course, those (and you may be amongst them) who can't help thinking that when a man mending an electricity pylon suddenly gets fried to a cinder on a pleasant summer's day, it's a decent bet that the pylon was responsible, rather than any rogue bolt of lightning. But, tempting as the theory is, the facts don't appear to bear it out.
Male Narrator: For a start, we have Edward's impeccable safety record - fifteen years up pylons and not so much as a tingle. What's more, the Health & Safety investigation was immediate and thorough, and found no evidence of human error or company negligence. And then we have the testimony of eighty-two year-old George Daniels, the nearest we have to an eye-witness, who swears that he saw a blinding flash of forked lightning crackle through the skies at around lunchtime when he was out walking his dog, Gerald.

Female Narrator: The controversy still rages today.
Male Narrator: Some simply won't buy the lightning theory at any price.
Female Narrator: Others question the testimony of anyone strange enough to call a dog Gerald.
Male Narrator: But, in a sense, it's all irrelevant.
Female Narrator: The fact is, Edward Jones was electrocuted, and no-one argues that, on the eve of his fortieth birthday, he had cheated death in the most spectacular

fashion.

Male Narrator: And that, ladies and gentlemen, is where our incredible story really begins…

Music link. Lights up to reveal Edward on the hospital bed. Mary, his wife, sits by him.

Male Narrator: Newhampton Hospital, three days later. The first thing Edward saw when he regained consciousness was a ham sandwich. And, approximately 30 inches behind it…his wife, Mary.

Mary: I've brought you some food, love - in case they weren't feeding you right.

Male Narrator: She smiled blandly.

Mary: How are you feeling?

Male Narrator: Excellent, he thought. Never better. As he slowly opened his mouth to respond, he felt his top lip split like a fat man's trousers. A small bead of blood popped out, and moistened his tongue. That's if it was his tongue. It felt like a badly barbecued sausage. He had to make every word count.

Edward: Where am I?
Mary: You're in hospital. One of your eyebrows is missing.

Male Narrator: Edward wondered if this was more a job for the police, rather than doctors, but was in no mood to quibble.

Edward: What happened?
Mary: You were electrocuted. Struck by lightning.

Male Narrator: Edward struggled to come to terms with the information. He didn't remember much about the incident, but subliminal fragments started flashing through his mind, like images from a crude flick book animation. A red tractor in a field. A ham sandwich. A butterfly. A harness on fire. Melted safety boots. A sense of blackness, and warmth. A strange smell. He couldn't visualize the smell, but he could smell it all right. Long after he'd lost the image of the butterfly, he'd remember that smell.

Mary: You were very lucky, they reckon.

Male Narrator: Oh, really? Being electrocuted and landing in a pile of shit is not everybody's idea of luck.

Mary: Anyway - seeing as how you missed it, best open this now. Happy birthday.

Mary hands Edward a card and a small, wrapped present.

Edward: What do you mean - missed it?
Mary: It was your birthday yesterday. I wanted to give you your present then, but the doctors said best not to disturb you - as you were unconscious.
Edward: Yesterday? You mean I've been out for three days?
Mary: Near enough. Go on, then. Open it.

Edward looks down at the small present. The very small present. No more than a few inches long, barely half an inch wide, and soft to the touch.

Edward: What is it? An eyebrow?
Mary: Open it!

His stiff and blackened fingers struggle to unravel the uninviting parcel. Finally he manages to pull out a tie clip.

Mary: It's a tie clip.
Edward: *(nonplussed)* Yes.
Mary: I always said you needed one.
Edward: Yes. Yes you always did.

Male Narrator: Now, a few words about this tie clip. It was made of eighteen carat gold - custom-made, in fact - in a sort of opened scroll shape, and engraved with Edward's name across the front in a richly ornate typeface. It cost over a hundred pounds. So, as tie clips go, it was up there with the best of them. But even though this tie clip might have entered our story in the guise of a gift, we all know that its real purpose is as a metaphor - a metaphor for the fact that all was not well with the Jones' marriage. Put simply, whereas Edward couldn't think of anything he'd like less for his fortieth birthday than a tie clip, Mary couldn't think of anything better. That was the difference between them. Small, but significant.

Mary: Well? Do you like it?

Male Narrator: Edward wanted with all his soul to say that it was the tackiest and most life denuding piece of shite he'd ever had the misfortune to clap his racoon eyes on. What he actually said was...

Edward: Erm...it's very...shiny.

Mary: It's gold. Eighteen carat.
Edward: That would account for it, then.
Mary: Try it on.
Edward: Maybe later.
Mary: All right, love. If you're tired.
Edward: Yes, I am tired. And my tongue feels like a sausage.
Mary: Well, I'm very sorry. I've only brought the ham.
Edward: No, I meant…it doesn't matter.

Enter Dr Rogers.

Rogers: I see you're back with us, Mr Jones. I'm Mr Rogers, the consultant. You had us worried for a while. Mind if I take a look around?
Edward: Help yourself.

The doctor produces a miniature torch, which he proceeds to shine deep into Edward's pupils at point blank range.

Rogers: Look up….down…straight ahead. Any pain?
Edward: Yes.
Rogers: Anywhere in particular?
Edward: Just the body.
Rogers: How's your memory, Edward?
Edward: Okay I think, Doctor er…
Rogers: …Rogers. Pop your tongue out for me. Mmm. I wouldn't put that back into your mouth if I were you.

The doctor snaps off his torch like a hypnotist snapping his fingers.

Rogers: And you must be Mrs Jones.
Mary: Oh, yes, doctor!

She addresses him as she would any royalty, pope or world leader.

Rogers: Well, your husband's had a very lucky escape. I'm going to hang on to him for another day or so, if that's all right - then we'll see what we can do about getting him home.
Mary: Thank you, doctor.
Rogers: Just drink plenty of water, and rest.
Mary: I will, doctor.
Rogers: No, I'm talking to Mr Jones now.
Mary: Oh, sorry doctor.

Rogers exits.

Mary: *(confidentially)* That was the consultant, Mr Rogers.
Edward: I know. He said.
Mary: He came to see you yesterday. But you were unconscious.
Edward: That's probably why I didn't recognize him.

Male Narrator: Now, having promised you such an incredible story, you'll no doubt be a tad disappointed to learn that, for a very long time, nothing happened. I say nothing - there were one or two minor developments worthy of note. Dr Rogers came back to see Edward a few days later, and was amazed by his progress. He was still badly charred, of course, but it was nothing a good session with a Brillo pad wouldn't sort out, and his heart, blood pressure and all other vital signs were as steady as a rock. So, he was released from hospital, with a note suggesting that he refrained from electrocuting himself for at least a fortnight, after which he could return to duty. Then, as I say, nothing happened. Edward scrubbed himself clean, re-grew his eyebrow, and went back to climbing pylons. Mary went back to making ham sandwiches every Friday. Everything was as it was. For five whole years. Even then, what happened next didn't get off to a particularly dramatic start. I mean, it wasn't one of those moments that make the audience gasp and jump - you know... *(SFX: a sudden loud shock chord)...* It was more of a sort of.... *(SFX: a slightly eerie drone)* ...moment - the sort that leaves the audience thinking "Something a bit weird's just happened but I don't know what it was." The moment in question occurred at 7.35pm, on Edward's forty-fifth birthday. *(Edward enters a separately spot lit area and begins acting out the scene)* Mary was taking him out for a meal. He was just putting the finishing touches to his new tie clip, when he suddenly had this strange... premonition.

We again hear the same eerie suspense note. Edward stops, and looks puzzled. He grabs a hand mirror and holds it above his head, angling it to get a better view. He fetches a Polaroid camera and curiously fumbles around trying to take a picture of the top of his own head. Mary shouts off-stage.

Mary: Edward...
Edward: Won't be a minute.

He waits for the picture to develop. The results are clearly puzzling him.

Mary: Edward!
Edward: Coming.

He pockets the Polaroid and exits.

A Flying Ducks Publication

Male Narrator: *(stepping into the spotlight)* Mmm. Time to visit the local doctor.

Music link. Lights cut to Edward and a female doctor at a desk.

Female Doctor: Mr Jones. I haven't seen you for a long time.
Edward: No. I've been ill. Sorry - old joke.
Female Doctor: Yes. Very.
Edward: Sorry.
Female Doctor: Now, let me see – last time I saw you it was for…a tetanus jab.
Edward: Yes.
Female Doctor: Mmm. Well?
Edward: Well, that worked – I didn't get tetanus.
Female Doctor: What can I do for you this time, Mr Jones?
Edward: Oh, right. Erm…this is going to sound silly.
Female Doctor: Probably. Try me.
Edward: Take a look at this.

He hands her a Polaroid.

Female Doctor: What is it?
Edward: It's a photograph.
Female Doctor: I realize that. What does it depict?
Edward: It's my head. The top of my head.

The doctor glances up and compares Edward's head with the photograph.

Female Doctor: So it is. And?
Edward: Bear with me. What do you see, in the photograph?
Female Doctor: The top of your head.
Edward: And what don't you see?
Female Doctor: Sydney Opera House. Can we get to the point?
Edward: All right – now take a look at this one.

He hands her another crumpled Polaroid.

Female Doctor: This one looks like a fuzzy picture of the moon.
Edward: It's my head again. That…is a bald patch.
Female Doctor: So?
Edward: So, that picture was taken ten years ago. We'd just had some new mirror wardrobes fitted and I accidentally caught sight of myself, through a hand mirror, from behind, as it were. I hadn't noticed it before.

Female Doctor: *(tetchily)* Why are you here, Mr Jones?
Edward: The bald patch. It was a bit of a shock, to be honest. It upset me. I ended up taking a picture of it, with my Polaroid. I got very depressed for a while, and then I decided...well, not to look any more. What you don't see can't hurt you, sort of thing. And that's how it's been. Until last Friday night. It was my birthday...
Female Doctor: Many happy returns...
Edward: Thank you, and something – I don't know what – well, I just had this urge to have another peek. Just to see how bad it was. I was expecting, you know, like a saucer or something. So, when I saw...well, that, I was shocked, really. In a sort of pleasant way. So, what do you think?
Female Doctor: What do I think about what?
Edward: All of it.
Female Doctor: Mr Jones, I've got patients waiting out there with illnesses.
Edward: I might be ill.
Female Doctor: I don't think so.
Edward: But my hair...
Female Doctor: Hair is not life threatening, Mr Jones.
Edward: Don't you think I should have my head examined?
Female Doctor: Don't tempt me, Mr Jones.
Edward: Aren't you at least going to take a look?

The doctor, clearly unimpressed, gets up. She ceremoniously dons some surgical gloves, then quickly glances at Edward's scalp without touching him and sits back down.

Female Doctor: There's nothing wrong with you.
Edward: But...what about the hair?
Female Doctor: These things can happen. Sometimes women lose their hair temporarily when they have psoriasis, but it grows back.
Edward: But I'm not a woman, and I haven't got psoriasis.
Female Doctor: Would you like something to help you sleep at night?
Edward: No. I sleep fine, thanks. Do you think I should see a specialist?

Male Narrator: That was it. Edward saw the doctor stiffen. For "Do you think I should see a specialist?" read "You're out of your depth, pal - move over and let a real doctor have a look." The doctor cut short the interview, offering the parting shot that Edward's tetanus jab could do with a booster. Edward knew where the tetanus jab was destined, and it was clear that revenge was on the doctor's mind, so he left while he still had his trousers on. *(Doctor and Edward exit)* But the incident only served to make him even more determined to get to the bottom of things, if that's the expression I want. That's when he thought of Rogers – the consultant. Very knowledgeable man, Rogers. He'd be far more sympathetic, reasoned Edward. So, next stop, the hospital.

Music link. Lights cut to female hospital receptionist, with Edward.

Receptionist: Mr Rogers, you say?
Edward: Yes. The consultant.
Receptionist: Have you got an appointment with Mr Rogers?
Edward: Erm, no…not exactly. I'd just like to talk to him for a moment.
Receptionist: Mr Rogers retired last year.
Edward: Oh.
Receptionist: But you wouldn't be the first to turn up for an appointment with him. That's the NHS for you - long waiting list, crap system. The I.T. people have been promising to sort it since last April, but it never happens. I've had three people after Mr Rogers this month already. And one woman came for her appointment with Mr Akerson, and he's been dead six years.
Edward: Right, well, can you tell me how I could get in touch with him?
Receptionist: Mr Akerson?
Edward: Mr Rogers.
Receptionist: Not allowed to give out addresses. Against hospital rules. Mr Akerson's a different matter, though. My sister is a well-respected clairvoyant, and…
Edward: But you could contact him – Mr Rogers?
Receptionist: In theory.
Edward: Right, then – put the theory into practice. Here's my number… and my name… please call Mr Rogers and tell him to get in touch with me as soon as possible.
Receptionist: But…
Edward: Tell him I'm the one who got struck by lightning – black face, one eyebrow, raccoon eyes, five years ago. Thank you for your time.

Exit Edward. Lights cut to Male Narrator.

Male Narrator: It was Friday. It was ham. And Edward was up a pylon when his mobile rang. It was Mr Rogers. Edward recognized those cultured tones instantly, and felt his heart give a little thump of excitement.

Edward: Thanks for ringing. I know you're retired, but I've got a condition which I think might interest you, from an intellectual point of view. I believe it's unique – potentially hugely significant, both medically and financially – but my own doctor is under-qualified and far too short-sighted to realize its importance. I'm not prepared to say any more over the phone. I'd like us to meet and discuss it face-to-face. Have you any time this week - later today perhaps, around four?

Male Narrator: The old Edward gasped in admiration at the new Edward. He was magnificent. Polite, but clinically to the point, and devastatingly authoritative. In this mood, Edward could sell double-glazing to Prince Charles. Rogers was putty in his hands, and instantly offered his address. An appointment was made for four o'clock that afternoon. The pylon with the dodgy connector would have to wait.

Music link. The Female Narrator takes up the story.

Female Narrator: A neatly coiffeured pair of topiary peacocks greeted Edward as he walked up the gravel driveway of Mr Rogers' elegant country retreat. Five years on, and out of the context of the hospital setting, Rogers looked far more frail than Edward had remembered. There was a vulnerability about him which instantly tinged Edward with sadness. That face, all that knowledge, at the mercy of such a fragile frame.

Rogers is pottering in his garden with pruning shears as Edward enters.

Edward: Very nice.
Rogers: Oh, Mr Jones, I presume?
Edward: Yes.
Rogers: Sorry, I don't remember the face. I thought I might. *(Walking indoors)* One of the side-effects of old age, I'm afraid. Do you know how many brain cells we lose every day, Mr Jones?
Edward: No.
Rogers: You'd be amazed. Erm...I can't seem to recall the exact figure myself any more. But it is a lot. Do make yourself at home. Would you like some tea?
Edward: No, thanks. I'm fine. I won't take up any more of your time than necessary, I just wanted an intelligent medical opinion on something that's happened to me. I think it's significant, but you might tell me it happens all the time and make me feel a complete fool. Either way, I'll trust your opinion. It all started, well...take a look at this photograph.

Edward hands over the bent and faded Polaroid. Mr Rogers takes a while to find focus, bringing it first close to his face, then away at arm's length, then taking it to the window for extra light, until he finally realizes that the image itself is not in focus.

Rogers: The moon?
Edward: My head. A bald patch.
Rogers: Ah. Yes. Yes, I see it now.
Edward: That was taken ten years ago, when I was thirty-five. Take a look at my head now.

A slightly wary Mr Rogers circles round to view Edward's head.

Rogers: Would you mind coming by the window, only my eyes...

Edward dutifully crouches down as Mr Rogers begins warming to his task.

Rogers: Would you mind if I...ruffled you up a bit?
Edward: Ruffle away.

Female Narrator: The ensuing examination is impressively thorough. At one point, Mr Rogers goes to a bureau and produces a large magnifying glass.

Rogers: You seem to have re-grown most of your hair.
Edward: Yes.
Rogers: The photograph – it's definitely you, I presume.
Edward: Yes.
Rogers: And you haven't taken any special medication over the last few years?
Edward: A few Lem Sips. Nothing else.
Rogers: Mmm.
Edward: Am I right - baldness is still pretty much a one-way ticket?
Rogers: In my experience, the only way a man can re-grow his own hair is with the help of triangular cuttings from his armpit. I take it you...
Edward: No. No armpit surgery.

Female Narrator: The doctor leaned forward with the magnifying glass for one last telling close-up by the window. Perfect timing, as the summer sun suddenly cut through a gap in the clouds, flooded the lens with pure energy, and singed a tiny laser beam dot into Edward's scalp.

Edward: Arrgh!
Rogers: Oh, I'm sorry. I'm so sorry. Do forgive me. Haven't done that in years. Used to set fire to leaves when I was a child. Are you all right?

Female Narrator: Edward was beginning to think he had somehow offended Nature. First he's struck by lightning, on a beautiful summer's day. Then he gets acute sunburn, in less than a second, whilst indoors. No longer trusting his luck, he began nervously scanning the carpet for wayward jelly fish.

Edward: So, what's the verdict – about the hair?
Rogers: Oh, yes. Mr Jones, I also have a Polaroid camera – would you mind?
Edward: Help yourself.

Exit Rogers.

Female Narrator: Polaroid cameras run on batteries, reasoned Edward. The chance of being wounded by one was remote. But then again, the chance of being struck by...

Mr Rogers is back, proudly clutching his camera.

Rogers: Would you mind crouching down? Lower. Lower. Just a little lower. *(There's a thud as Edward's head hits the seat)* That's it. Stay exactly as you are, please.

Female Narrator: The genial doctor was taking great care to get exactly the same angle as the original photograph. Edward knew he'd come to the right man. But he was wrong about the chances of being wounded by a Polaroid camera. They are, of course, considerably larger than conventional cameras, and while having one dropped directly onto your skull from two and a half feet is never perhaps going to be life-threatening, it's certainly no picnic.

Rogers drops the camera on Edward's head, polaxing him. Rogers apologizes profusely.

Female Narrator: The doctor's arthritic fingers, struggling to find the ideal camera position, had momentarily lost their grip on the casing, and it was only then that Edward realized just how painful arthritis can be. It was becoming increasingly clear why retirement had been the only sensible option for this once fine surgeon. Eventually, the shot was taken. But only after Edward had carefully masked off all the superfluous parts of his head with pillows. The doctor looked well-pleased with the results, and carefully signed and dated the new evidence, in ink, on the back.

Rogers: The date's important you see because, well, look here. See? It looks to all intents and purposes like a typical case of male pattern baldness, before and after. But it's in reverse. The before should be the after, and the after the before. Fascinating. I'd like to show these to a friend of mine - Jack Nugent. He's a trichologist.

Female Narrator: Excellent, thought Edward. He'd been recommended to a circus act.

Rogers: He'll probably want to examine you himself, if that's all right?

Female Narrator: Edward wasn't sure if he could survive another examination without investing in a motorcycle helmet, but nodded appreciatively. Rogers was a good man. A tad clumsy, perhaps, and a few years past the surgeon's equivalent of a sell-by date, but good. As Edward said his goodbyes and strolled back up the gravel path to his van, more subtle evidence of Rogers' unfortunate demise confronted him.

He hadn't noticed before, but one of the topiary peacocks was missing its head. A momentary slip with the clippers, no doubt. A lifetime of cultivation blighted in an instant by a frustrating combination of uncertain hands and failing eyesight.

Edward: Sad. But I suppose old age comes to us all.

Female Narrator: It would be another two weeks before Edward realized the extraordinary irony of what he'd just said.

Music link. We see Edward working on the pylon.

Edward's appointment with Jack Nugent came astonishingly quickly. It came by phone, and it came within twenty-four hours. Edward's mobile went just as he was tucking into a ham sandwich. It was Friday.

Nugent: Mr Jenkins?
Edward: Jones.
Nugent: Oh, sorry. I was told Jenkins. My name's Ted Nugent. I'm a doctor. Mr Rogers asked me to get in touch.
Edward: Oh. Right. I was expecting you. Only not so soon. And he said your name was Jack.
Nugent: Yes, right. I'm afraid Peter's memory is getting a little slippy these days, bless him. He called me John when he rang. But I am Ted. Edward, actually. And you are?
Edward: Edward.
Nugent: Oh, right. Easy enough then.

Female Narrator: Formal introductions over, Ted made an appointment for Edward to see him three days later at the hospital. Three days? Had he urgently needed a new hip, or a replacement heart valve, he would no doubt have languished at the end of an elastic queue. But here he was, offering the merest sniff of a condition which could add value to a consultant's reputation or bank account, and he was being hurriedly strapped into an NHS rocket ship bound for the top man.

Enter Nugent.

Female Narrator: Ted Nugent, consultant trichologist.

Edward knocks and enters.

Nugent: Edward!
Edward: Mr Nugent?
Nugent: *[Disappointed?

Edward: Er…no, I…
Nugent: Let me guess. You weren't expecting your hair specialist to be completely bald.
Edward: Well…
Nugent: Think about it, Edward. Scratch below the surface. A completely bald hair specialist is just the sort of bloke you want on your side. He understands the problem. He's driven by the right sort of emotions. He's not just an interested bystander – he's a genuine shareholder, he owns a slice of the action. Nevertheless, you're disappointed.
Edward: No, I…
Nugent: I know…it's like having an appointment with an ugly beauty therapist, or a fat keep-fit instructor. It shouldn't reflect on their ability to teach the subject, but deep down you're thinking, if he's so damn good, why does he still look like a snooker ball?
Edward: I'm not questioning…
Nugent: It's human nature, Edward. You want your beauty therapist to be beautiful, in the same way that you want your hair specialist to be hairy. As a totem. A sign of hope.
Edward: Look, I…
Nugent: Let me tell you something, Edward. You'll soon learn that modesty is not amongst my long list of qualities. As a young man in the world of science and medicine I was seriously hot news. I could have been anything I wanted. And then… this happened. This, Edward, is the reason I do what I do.
Edward: Okay, okay. Qualifications accepted.
Nugent: Not that you have my problem.
Edward: No, more the opposite really.
Nugent: And that is what intrigues me.]* May I?
Edward: Help yourself.

Nugent takes just the briefest glimpse at Edward's crown.

Nugent: Mmm.
Edward: Is that it?
Nugent: *[What - disappointed in me again?
Edward: Well, I did think…]*
Nugent: No. No I haven't finished with you yet, Edward. Not quite. There's a screen back there. Strip to the underpants.

A shocked Edward disappears.

Female Narrator: Nugent, in short, was magnificent. Edward felt like his entire being - mind, body and soul - had been nibbled into small pieces and taken away for analysis by a huge army of professor ants. No quick glance at the scalp under a bright light for this man - oh, no. Blood pressure, weight, saliva, urine and blood samples, armpit swabs, lung capacity, ear nose and throat exploration, nail clippings, foot scrapings, retina scans, chest hair cuttings – everything which could legally be done to a living body in the pursuit of science was done at least once, sometimes twice for luck.

Edward re-enters fastening his shirt.

Nugent: *(examining data)* Well, Edward, I think we've made a good start.
Edward: Start?
Nugent: I shall have to do all this again, I'm afraid, in a week's time. Comparative data, you see.

Female Narrator: Edward wasn't sure that he did see. But he duly attended another intensive session, seven days later, just as rigorous as the last.

Nugent: Right. That should be all I need. I'll be in touch in a week or so. *(He offers Edward his hand)* Don't worry.
Edward: Should I be worried?
Nugent: Erm…no.
Edward: Now I'm worried.
Nugent: Don't be. I'll get to the bottom of it.

Female Narrator: The door closed abruptly, but through its small glass panel Edward caught sight of Nugent rushing straight back to his desk, where he'd already begun examining a pulsating mass of graphical data flashing on the screen of his laptop. Wow. This was one excited scientist.

Male Narrator: Edward decided to take the rest of the day off. He didn't go home, just for a walk around some nearby parkland. He wanted some air, some space, some quality thinking time. He hadn't confided in Mary since this whole business began. She wouldn't understand, he reasoned. She rarely understood.

Mary: How was your day?
Edward: All right.
Mary: Mend any pylons?
Edward: A few.
Mary: Good.

Male Narrator: Their long chat over, Mary returned to the hypnotic spell of the television and the comfort of her box of chocolates. As Edward glanced over, what he saw disturbed him. He hadn't really noticed it before – perhaps he just hadn't looked. But there was no denying it. In the last few years, Mary's face had imperceptibly morphed from youthful middle age to early old age. His wife had become Aunty Joan. There was a time that Mary treated her body like a temple. Now, the temple had been closed and converted into a Bingo Hall.

Edward acts out the next few moments.

In a quiet state of panic, Edward jumped up and made his way to the bathroom. He tugged on the light cord, but kept his eyes tight shut, daring not to look. Finally, he plucks up courage and examines himself in the mirror. No. Not him. Not yet. Thank God. Not even allowing for a generous portion of bias, Edward was convinced that he was not staring at an old man in the making. His wife may be Aunty Joan, but he had not yet become Uncle Peter and, for that at least, he quietly gave thanks.

Music link. The lights fade on a pensive Edward.

Female Narrator: In fact, Edward was generally feeling quite energized of late. He had a spring in his step and a sharpness in his thinking which he hadn't felt for years. Some mornings he was only a heartbeat away from singing in the shower. Smiling was surely just around the corner. If these were the early rumblings of his mid-life crisis, bring it on.

We see Edward climbing the pylon behind the narrator.

Male Narrator: The working week melted away, and it seemed like no time at all before Edward was once again enjoying the familiar delights of a high-altitude ham sandwich. As he watched the long, frustrated snake of Friday afternoon traffic slowly wriggle its way along the motorway, his mobile rang. But he didn't answer it. Why should he? He didn't hear it. He'd left his mobile in the van, sixty feet below.

Female Narrator: And thus it was that, while an unsuspecting maintenance man nonchalantly watched the world go by from the comfort of his Gloucestershire pylon, seventy miles away an anxious doctor was taking a deep breath, steadying his nerve, and preparing to leave the world's most extraordinary voice-mail.

Spotlight on Nugent.

Nugent: Edward, it's Ted Nugent. Erm... I've managed to... I think I've... you've...the thing is... what's actually... the reason you're... when you... the tests were... can you call me back?

A puzzled and worried Edward is listening to the message.

Female Narrator: Nugent definitely sounded anxious. Like a man with bad news to impart. But this was no ordinary bearer of bad news – this was a doctor. Let's face it, on the I've got some bad news for you Richter scale, doctors hit a maximum ten every time - altogether a different league from the mild tremors caused by your accountant, or the man doing your MOT. All sorts of uneasy thoughts whirred through Edward's mind. Had Nugent found some dread disease? Is there such a thing as hair cancer? As he heard the doctor's voice, all the moisture in his mouth suddenly took a holiday.

Nugent: Edward?
Edward: Yes.
Nugent: Thanks for ringing back. Erm...I've completed the tests.
Edward: Yes.
Nugent: Look, I'll get straight to the point.
Edward: Yes.
Nugent: Can you come and see me on Monday morning?
Edward: Yes.
Nugent: Good. Nine o'clock?
Edward: Yes...
Nugent: Can't really explain over the phone, but erm...interesting stuff. See you Monday, yes?
Edward: Yes.
Nugent: Goodnight.
Edward: Yes.

Female Narrator: Edward sat on the side of the road in his van, staring at his mobile as if it had just betrayed him. The most important conversation of his life, and all he could manage was one word. Yes. Terrific. He could have performed his part in the dialogue just as well at eighteen months old.

Edward: Hold on to the positives, Edward. Don't get carried away. He said he'll see me on Monday. So that means I'll still be alive on Monday. But maybe not on Tuesday. But surely he would have told me if I was d...but on the other hand...

Female Narrator: He couldn't stand it. He was ringing Nugent back.

Edward: Come on. Come on, damn it, answer. Shit. Voice mail. Do I leave a message? Do I ask him if he's in the toilet? Do I ask him if he's gone home? Do I ask him if I'm going to die? Dr Nugent, it's Edward Jones. Erm...can you call me back?

Female Narrator: But Nugent didn't. He was on his way home to his pipe and slippers. And it was the longest weekend of Edward's life.

Lights fade down and back up. Music link.

Nine o'clock Monday morning, as agreed, Edward, complete with packed lunch, was waiting outside Nugent's office. Actually, Edward was a tad early. It was six-fifteen. But you couldn't blame an anxious man for being a little impatient. Nugent was also early. He arrived at five to nine.

Nugent: My God, you look dreadful!

Female Narrator: The perfect way to settle Edward's nerves.

Nugent: You'd better come in.

As they enter the office, Edward slams the door, pins Nugent to the wall, and clasps his cheeks firmly in both hands to ensure unfailing eye contact.

Edward: I need to know. Now!
Nugent: Okay. Okay. I'm soggy.

Nugent's voice is cruelly distorted through two squashed cheeks. Edward slowly releases his grip, but his stare continues to hold the doctor in a vice-like grip.

Edward: You're soggy?
Nugent: I didn't realize I'd got you so worried. Sit down.
Edward: No, not sit down. Anything but sit down. I'm going to die, aren't I?
Nugent: No, it's nothing like that, it's…it's…different. Look, will you please sit down?

Edward faints, face down. Nugent panics when he retrieves his hand from Edward's face to reveal it is covered in blood.

Nugent: Oh my God!

Nugent goes woozy, and also faints, landing face down right on top of Edward. The impact brings Edward round, looking rather startled. A female nurse enters, and is initially not sure what she's witnessing.

Nurse: Holy Mary, mother of God. Mr Nugent! Mr Nugent? What on earth's going on here?

Nugent is hauled up to reveal that he too has blood all over his face.

Nurse: Mr Nugent! What happened to him?
Edward: I think he fainted and banged his nose.
Nurse: And what happened to you?
Edward: I think I fainted and banged my nose.
Nurse: *(putting Nugent's head between his legs)* I've never seen anything like it. Grown men. *(Passing Edward some tissues)* Get yourself sat down. Here. Hold that tightly on the bridge of the nose.

Edward reaches for Nugent's nose.

Nurse: Yours - not his!
Edward: Sorry.
Nurse: Head up! Mr Nugent - are you with us?
Nugent: What happened?
Nurse: You came second in a fainting competition. Here, hold this tightly on the bridge. Sit up here.

The nurse deals with the two men as if they're two big kids after a fight. She gets them both sat down, side by side, heads in the air, clutching their noses tightly with a wad of tissues.

Nurse: There. I think you'll both live. Can I get along to my ward now?
Nugent: Has it stopped?
Nurse: It will. Keep your head up.
Nugent: I think we'll be all right now. Thank you, sister.
Nurse: You're welcome. I'll send somebody along to get this floor mopped. It's absolutely swimming in blood.

Nurse exits. Nugent, hearing the nurse's proclamation, faints again, slumping to the floor. Edward, with his head up, hasn't noticed at first that he's gone.

Edward: Mr Nugent...
Nugent: *(fainting)* Uhhh!
Edward: No, please, don't interrupt. I need to say this. The thing is, I know that something very serious is wrong with me. I've been worrying about it all weekend, and now, well, to be honest I'm too emotionally drained to worry about it any more. I'm prepared for the worst. So you can tell me now. Mr Nugent? Mr...

Edward looks down and sees that Nugent is unconscious.

Edward: Oh, bugger! Mr Nugent! Nurse!!!

Edward grapples to bring Nugent round and get him back on the seat.

Nugent: What happened?
Edward: You fainted. Again. At least you didn't bang your nose this time.
Nugent: *(eyes shut)* I'm sorry. I've never been any good dealing with blood.
Edward: But you're a doctor.
Nugent: I'm a hair doctor. Hair doesn't bleed. Just the way I am, I'm afraid. I daren't look, in case I go again. Has it…stopped?
Edward: I think so. Just hold… *(Edward goes to hand Nugent a very blood-stained tissue, but thinks better of it)* …keep your eyes shut. *(He looks around for an alternative, but can find nothing other than more blood-stained tissues. In desperation, he grabs one of the cheese sandwiches from his lunchbox and squeezes it onto Nugent's nose)* Okay, just hold that on. Head up. Keep your eyes tightly shut.
Nugent: You must think I'm a real wimp.
Edward: No, I just think it's weird. I mean, when you were doing my tests, you took, like…
Nugent: Blood tests. That's different. That's needles. I can deal with that. That's under my control. Everything neatly labelled in glass containers. It's the uncontrolled stuff that gets to me. When it starts…squirting out from… *(he starts to slump)*
Edward: All right! All right. Change the subject. Come on. Think about something nice. Think about…baby puppies.
Nugent: Baby puppies?
Edward: Well, I just thought…
Nugent: I don't like dogs.
Edward: All right, let's talk about me instead. Why don't you just…remove the cheese sandwich from your nose, and tell me what you've got to tell me. And don't hold back.

Nugent, though initially bewildered to find he has a cheese sandwich in his hand, finally acknowledges Edward's frustration with a gentle nod, and stands to deliver his big speech.

Nugent: The problem is, Edward, I don't think you'd believe me if I told you.
Edward: Try me.
Nugent: Losing hair is a natural part of the ageing process in men, like going grey, or wrinkly. But your hair, against all the normal laws of nature, has grown back…
Edward: *(impatiently)* Yes, but did you find the reason?
Nugent: Yes.
Edward: And?
Nugent: And it was not what I was expecting. I was expecting it might have something

to do with the blood flow through the tiny capillaries...

Edward: Mr Nugent...Ted. Please. I've been crawling the walls since Friday night. Please, don't tell me what it isn't. I need to know what it is.

Nugent: Very well. There are a thousand and one indicators of ageing, Edward. For example, DNA mutations are more likely the older a cell is, simply because every time a cell divides it is vulnerable to damage, so older cells will have undergone more divisions.

Edward: I'm not with you.

Nugent: Well, most cells are programmed to reproduce a fixed number of times and then die by a sort of cell suicide, a process we call apoptosis. Apoptosis can be triggered abnormally by some DNA mutations...

Edward: Woah! Hold it right there! I wasn't with you before, remember?

Nugent: It's to do with cell damage and...you see we can measure this quite accurately now and...well, the samples you gave me the first week, compared to the samples from the second week...oh, just look at this graph...

Edward: No. Don't give me graphs. Give me facts. Give me a simple sentence!

Nugent: Simple's hard! Look, the science is a little complicated, but the facts are undeniable. In a nutshell, Edward...

Edward: Yes! Give it me in a nutshell. A nice, tiny, bite-sized nutshell.

Nugent: Okay. You are, as far as I can ascertain, doing what no other human being in the history of, well, of human beings, has ever done before. Or animals. Or plants...

Edward: What sort of nut is this? A coconut? Give me a peanut!

Nugent: All right! In a word, you, Edward Jones are, to all intents and purposes...

Edward: A word! You said a word!!

Nugent: Getting younger!

Female Narrator: Nugent thought it wise to pause for a moment, while the gist of his statement sank in. It didn't.

Edward: I'm still not with you.

Nugent: No, I'm not really surprised. Edward, how old are you?

Edward: Forty-five.

Nugent: I don't think so.

Edward: What?

Nugent: I don't dispute you were born forty-five years ago. But when was the last time you looked in a mirror?

Edward: This weekend.

Nugent: And did you see a man of forty-five? Or did you see what I see – a man in his mid-thirties?

Edward: Well...I...

Nugent: Edward, I have found indisputable scientific evidence that your whole metabolism is operating in reverse. Your hair is growing back because you are getting younger instead of older. And it's my guess that this has been happening for at least the past five years. It's not just your hair. It's every cell in your body.

Female Narrator: Edward stared at him - a huge, complex, bewildered stare. Nugent stared back – a sympathetic, exhausted, I totally understand your need to stare at me in that complex, bewildered way sort of stare. Neither felt it appropriate to say anything else for five whole minutes. Finally, Edward broke the ice with a simple elegance.

Edward: How do I know you're not just talking bollocks?
Nugent: You don't.
Edward: Who else have you told about this?
Nugent: No-one.
Edward: So you could be wrong.
Nugent: Possibly. Probably. But I don't see how. I've been over the results a thousand times.

Another long silence.

Edward: So, if I'm getting younger – well, that's good news – isn't it?
Nugent: Erm...up to a point.
Edward: Up to a point? What do you mean? What point? It's everyone's dream, right? I'm not going to get older, and weaker. I'm getting younger, and stronger.

Nugent slowly turns away to face the window.

Nugent: Edward, can you remember what you did yesterday?
Edward: Of course I can, why?
Nugent: And the day before?
Edward: Yes.
Nugent: So your memory's fine?
Edward: Yes. What's my memory got to do with it?
Nugent: Everything, unfortunately. (*Nugent wheels round*) Yes, on the face of it, what you say is true. Getting younger is everyone's dream. How many times have we all wished we were ten years younger? But you see, even though your body has gone into reverse, your mind hasn't. You remember yesterday, and the day before, which means that your mind - your psychology - is moving forwards, acquiring experience and knowledge in the normal manner, chronologically. Put simply, your body is getting younger, but your mind is still getting older. If this continues – and I'm not saying it will – but if it does, then physically you'll be thirty again, twenty-five again, twenty. But your mind...your personality, will be fifty, fifty-five, sixty. Can't you see?

Edward, gradually realizing that his imminent death sentence has been lifted, suddenly feels in combative mood.

Edward: Yes, I can see. You're saying I get another crack at youth, but with all the benefit of knowledge and experience. That's brilliant.
Nugent: Brilliant? Yes, maybe. As I say, up to a point. I suspect there may some good times ahead for you – some amazing times. But think it through, Edward. Think about the psychological impact. You're going to need counselling.
Edward: Counselling? Don't be ridiculous. I'll be on cloud nine.
Nugent: But your wife, your friends – they'll all be going the other way. You'll have no permanent companionship.
Edward: I can live with that. I've always been a bit of a loner.
Nugent: You'll need to be. Because one day, you're going to find yourself to be an old-age pensioner in a teenager's body.
Edward: Great. I'd be the ultimate dirty old man.
Nugent: Do you really want to go back to school when you're sixty-five?
Edward: I won't need school. I'll be educated.
Nugent: And what happens when you're a toddler?
Edward: I'll just stay at home and play with my toys. The perfect retirement.
Nugent: And who'll be your mom when you're three?
Edward: Who cares, I…
Nugent: And what happens three years later?
Edward: I…

Edward is stopped in his tracks.

Nugent: Is that what you want, Edward? To celebrate your eightieth year, your final birthday party, in an incubator, shrinking, waiting for a nine month reduction back into a sperm?
Edward: Are you trying to tell me this is going to go all the way?
Nugent: I don't know, Edward. I have no idea why this happened, whether it will last, or if it can be reversed. Look, I was hoping to brief you on this in a more controlled fashion, but…
Edward: The lightning.
Nugent: What?
Edward: I was struck by lightning. Five years ago. My fortieth birthday. Everybody said I was lucky to survive. That's when it all started. I'm sure it is.
Nugent: Lightning?
Edward: A bolt from the blue.

Female Narrator: As Nugent's face absorbed this precious new data, he went so deep into thought that he slipped into an altered state of consciousness.

Edward, noticing that his companion was no longer willing to take part in any meaningful dialogue, waves a hand in front of his face.

Edward: Mr Nugent. Ted.

Female Narrator: It was no use. Nugent had clearly locked himself away and slipped a huge 'Do Not Disturb' sign over his eyes. Edward sensed that something vital was happening, and decided to respect his privacy. It was two whole minutes before Nugent re-appeared. When he did, he walked slowly towards the window.

Edward: Are you all right?
Nugent: *(turning)* Edward, I'm about to ask you the most difficult question imaginable, and I need an answer.
Edward: If it's algebra, forget it. *(Nugent doesn't react to Edward's attempt to lighten the mood)* Go on.
Nugent: If I could find a way, do you want me to reverse this?
Edward: Can it be done?
Nugent: Possibly. But you're going to need to be incredibly brave.

Edward takes a deep breath. There's a distant thunder crack, and lightning flashes illuminate the pylon behind them.

Edward: What do I have to do?

There's a swell of dramatic music. Curtain. End of Act One.

Act Two

A lady is out walking her "dog". The dog is represented by the old trick stiff lead and collar prop, which makes the dog look invisible. Enter Male Narrator.

Male Narrator: Sarah Appleby was out walking her dog when her house exploded.

There's a huge explosion. Small fragments of debris fall from the skies. Sarah looks into the distance, dismayed but clearly not surprised.

Sarah: Oh, bollocks.

Male Narrator: It was a lucky escape – five minutes earlier she was in the kitchen, attempting to attach the lead to the dog collar. If her spaniel had been its normal unruly self, both master and canine companion would have ended up scattered across the nearby fields in kit form. Nothing remained of the house except a black, smoking dent in the ground. The television aerial, which had always leaned a few degrees from the vertical, was launched like a sky rocket and claimed the only casualty, a passing crow, harpooning it to an oak tree.

Sound effect – a crow harpooned to a tree.

Sarah: Come on, Jack. Not much point going home now. Let's see if we can find a phone box, eh?

Sarah exits.

Male Narrator: Now, to those that knew her, none of this came as a surprise. Sarah, you see, liked to...experiment. Ever since she was a toddler, she'd been strangely intrigued by all things scientific. While other little girls were out playing hopscotch, Sarah would be in her bedroom, randomly mixing together the sort of chemicals that came out of padlocked lead containers marked with a skull and crossbones, just to see what would happen. And if nothing particularly exciting resulted, she would try applying a naked flame, or an electrical current, just to spice up the evening. So it was no coincidence that she lived so remotely - in fact, most of the locals firmly believed that Sarah was a witch.

And this wasn't the first time one of her experiments had gone badly wrong. Sarah's activities first achieved notoriety when she was just six years old. It made all the local papers. Her grandmother, halfway through wishing her old friend Mrs Perkins a Merry Christmas, spontaneously combusted in the supermarket. The incident baffled detectives and scientists alike, until it was eventually discovered that old ma Appleby had accidentally sipped one of Sarah's potions instead of her Yuletide sherry at the family party, and this had caused her to become unstable. Nothing was ever proven, of course.

Sarah enters, still with the "dog".

So, is she a witch? A misunderstood scientist? Or is she just totally off her trolley? After all, why else would she take an empty dog collar for a walk?

The Male Narrator has stooped to point to the collar. A dark barks and he quickly withdraws his hand.

There's more to this lady than meets the eye.

Sarah: Come on, Jack - there's a cottage over there.

Exit Sarah and dog.

Male Narrator: A neatly coiffeured pair of topiary peacocks greeted Sarah and her dog as they walked up the gravel driveway of the elegant country retreat. Neat, that is, except for the fact that one of the peacocks was missing its head. Sound familiar?

Sarah enters and rings a doorbell.

[Excuse me. I need to get that.]

Male Narrator exits.

Sarah: *(tying the lead to a post)* Sorry, Jack. I'm going to have to leave you here. They just wouldn't understand.

The dog barks obediently.

Rogers: *(from off-stage)* Who's there?
Sarah: It's Sarah Appleby, from across the common. I was wondering if I could use your phone, only...mine's not working.

Male Narrator enters as Rogers.

Rogers: Sarah Appleby – from Grange Lane?
Sarah: That's me.
Rogers: Oh – right. I've heard a lot about you.
Sarah: Yes, I bet you have.
Rogers: Don't worry. I don't believe any of it. Superstitious nonsense. Well, come in, do. Erm...on your own?
Sarah: Yes.
Rogers: Oh. That wasn't your dog I heard?
Sarah: No. Witches only have black cats.
Rogers: Yes, so they do.

The dog barks.

Rogers: I think your cat just barked again.
Sarah: Must be a stray.
Rogers: Trouble with your phone, you say?
Sarah: Yes, it's erm...well, it stopped working when my house exploded.
Rogers: Exploded? Good Lord. That wasn't your bang I heard a few minutes ago was it?
Sarah: 'Fraid so. One of my experiments appears to have, well, back-fired.
Rogers: Is the house badly hurt?
Sarah: I don't think it felt a thing. Completely evaporated.
Rogers: Goodness me. Erm...whom did you want to phone?
Sarah: Well, just a local hotel for now. I'll start picking up the pieces tomorrow, when it's light.
Rogers: How dreadful. My dear girl. But look, I've got a spare room here – least I can do is give you shelter for the night.
Sarah: Well, I don't want to be any trouble.
Rogers: No trouble I assure you, I'd welcome the company. And, delightful as you are, my dear, I can assure you I'm well past the age where I might try any funny business.
Sarah: You're very sweet.
Rogers: Now then – whisky, port, sherry - or would you prefer tea?
Sarah: Whisky's fine.
Rogers: Excellent. There we are, then. Well, Miss er...Appletree – or may I call you Suzie?
Sarah: Erm...yes, Suzie's fine.
Rogers: Well, Suzie - call me a nosy old parker if you like, but I take quite a bit of interest in science myself, and if you've got the time and the energy, I'd love to hear all about your experiment.

Music Link. Lights fade on the two of them. A spotlight picks out a telephone, which is ringing repeatedly. Eventually it is answered by a groggy Edward in a dressing gown.

Edward: Hello?
Nugent: *(off-stage, talking through the megaphone to give a telephone voice effect)* Edward. It's Ted Nugent.
Edward: Bloody hell - it's six o'clock in the morning!
Nugent: Listen very carefully. Do not, I repeat, do not, get seen, but take a very sneaky look out of your window.

He does.

Edward: Arrgh! What the hell's going on?
Nugent: I take it you're surrounded.
Edward: Who are they?
Nugent: Reporters. Don't ask me how, but the cat's out of the bag. Your story's all over the front pages.
Edward: What?
Nugent: Listen to these headlines: The Sun: *Medical Freak Defies Ageing Process.* The Mirror leads with *The Incredible Shrinking Man.* The Guardian: *Real-Life Dorian Gray Shocks the World.*
Edward: But who told them?
Nugent: Not me. And I presume not you.
Edward: No!
Nugent: This is big, Edward. Out of control. My office has been broken into. All my notes have been stolen. We have to meet.
Edward: Where?
Nugent: The park opposite the hospital. Can you slip out without being followed?
Edward: *(dramatically)* I'll find a way.

Female Narrator: So, the story was out. But how? Well, the trouble is, everyone knows at least one person they can trust with a secret and consequently the troubled Nugent had confided in his wife, Agnes.
Male Narrator: Agnes, of course, wouldn't dream of telling a soul, so she was careful to warn her friend Brenda that she mustn't tell a soul.
Female Narrator: Not that Brenda would dream of breathing a word of it to anyone. Except her best friend, Clara.
Male Narrator: Clara, sworn to secrecy, made sure that she only told people she could trust to keep a secret.
Female Narrator: And those she told only passed it on to those whom they trusted not to pass it on to anyone who would pass it on to anyone who would pass it on.
Male Narrator: Thus it was that, eight days later, the greatest secret of the modern

world hit the front pages of the tabloids. Meanwhile, Edward's wife Mary awoke to find herself besieged by paparazzi.

Mary groggily wanders in wearing a dressing gown.

Mary: Edward? Edward? What's all that noise? Edward?

She peeks out of the window, and screams. Lights cut to black. As the lights come back up, the Male Narrator takes up the story. Mary mimes the actions to his words.

Male Narrator: Distressed and bewildered, Mary searched the house for Edward. What she found was not Edward, but an open bedroom window, next to a drainpipe, and a hastily ransacked wardrobe. Her wardrobe. Yes, they were her clothes that Edward had left strewn all over the bed. But not all of them. The pink trouser suit was missing. The awful truth suddenly hit her. She lay down on the bed and cried herself back to sleep.

Music link.

Several hours later, she woke with a start. A hand was touching her. It was her brother, Martin.

Mary: Ugh!
Martin: It's only me.
Mary: Martin!
Martin: It's all right. I told them all to bugger off. I told them nobody's talking. And I told them Edward's not here.
Mary: He's not. He escaped.

She points woefully towards the window. Martin sits beside her.

Martin: Have you seen the papers yet?
Mary: No. But I know.
Martin: It's unbelievable, isn't it.
Mary: Over twenty years together, Martin. And never once did I get a hint of it.
Martin: Well, it only started a few years ago, apparently.
Mary: But why?
Martin: Nobody seems to know. One paper said it was something to do with him being hit by lightning.
Mary: That's ridiculous.
Martin: Jolted his metabolism or something.

Mary's trembling bottom lip finally gives way to a flood of tears. Martin, never quite comfortable in the comforting department, gently pats her head.

Martin: Come on, Mary...
Mary: It's me, isn't it. I've caused all this.
Martin: Don't be daft, Mary. How could you have caused it?
Mary: I'm not stupid, Martin. A man doesn't suddenly start dressing in women's clothes unless there's something...missing at home.

Martin's hand pats its last pat.

Martin: What do you mean?
Mary: Well, there are plenty of transvestites out there, Martin. You can't tell me they've all been struck by lightning.
Martin: Transvestites? Trans-bloody-vestites? What the bloody hell's this got to do with trans-chuffin-vestites?
Mary: Edward's problem. I thought you knew. He's run off in my pink trouser suit.

A bewildered Martin produces a creased-up copy of a newspaper from his pocket and hands it to her.

Martin: Here – I think you'd better read this.

Lights down. Music link. The lights fade up to reveal an uncomfortable-looking Edward, badly disguised as a woman, dressed in Mary's pink trouser suit and hat. We hear Nugent's urgent whisper from off-stage.

Nugent: Edward!
Edward: Ted?
Nugent: Don't look round. Thank God you had the sense to come in disguise. These people are everywhere. We can't talk here. I'll meet you over by those bushes - by the pond. Just try to look nonchalant.

Edward tries. Eventually Nugent appears, also wearing female clothing, including a skirt and hat.

Nugent: We mustn't draw attention to ourselves.
Edward: Oh, that's all right then. Two six-foot transvestites dressed for a wedding shouldn't draw much of a crowd.
Nugent: Here.

He hands Edward a round of bread.

Edward: *(biting into it ravenously)* Thanks.
Nugent: It's not for you! Feed the ducks. And just keep smiling. How did you get here?
Edward: I stole the next door neighbour's car. He always leaves the keys in.
Nugent: Do you think you were followed?
Edward: Not sure. One car did look a bit suspicious, but….
Nugent: But what?
Edward: Well, he was in front of me.
Nugent: This is bloody mad, Edward. I don't know how it could have leaked out.
Edward: Well don't look at me. I didn't even tell my wife.
Nugent: Well neither did… *(his eyes widen)* …all right, what's done's done. We need to find a way out of this mess. Nice trouser suit, by the way.
Edward: Thank you.
Nugent: Pink suits you.

Nugent and Edward wander off stage. Spotlight on Female Narrator.

Female Narrator: Now, the last thing either man wanted at that moment was to be approached by the park drunk offering them money for sex. But what we want and what we get are often opposite poles. The drunk simply wouldn't take "Bugger off" for an answer. He took a particular shine to the younger-looking Edward, and tried placing a groping hand on his knee. Edward's response, no doubt fuelled by acute stress and a massive adrenalin rush, was a swift and decisive chinning, which sent the drunk skidding headlong down the grassy bank until he eventually came to rest in the water feature.

Enter Nugent and Edward. Edward is rubbing a painful fist.

Nugent: Great! We're supposed to be trying not to draw attention to ourselves here!
Edward: I've been through a lot in the last few weeks, Ted. I am not having sex with a man just to keep him quiet. Especially one that's been drinking.
Nugent: He could be undercover.
Edward: Well, now he's underwater. Either way, he's out of commission.
Nugent: We need to get out of here before he wakes up.
Edward: Where are we going?
Nugent: Come on – I've got an idea. We'll need your car.
Edward: I've told you. It's not my car.
Nugent: Even better.

Female Narrator: Nugent's idea was to hide out somewhere remote. A friend's house. A friend Nugent could trust. Edward flung his neighbour's stolen car dramatically round the country lanes like a man desperately trying to defend a two second lead in the RAC rally.

We see Nugent and Edward sat on the bench seat facing forward, dramatically acting out the car scene.

Nugent: *(frantically barking instructions)* Next left...two hundred yards, into third, sharp right...accelerate...accelerate! Canal bridge! Woah! *(They lift up from the seat as if they've left the ground)* Okay - hard right next. *(Edward swings the wheel but is stopped by Nugent)* Not yet!
Edward: When?
Nugent: When we hit the floor...

They hit the floor with a bang and Edward frantically swings the steering wheel round.

Nugent: Okay - into fourth...fifty yards. Into third...twenty yards. Into second. Left. Left! Hard left! Even harder left! Watch out for that... *(there's a sickening thud, and the sound of an engine hissing steam)* ...tree.
Edward: Bollocks! Jim's going to kill me.
Nugent: Leave it. We can walk the rest.

Female Narrator: As they rounded the corner, Edward suddenly recognized the territory. He knew that house. He recognized that gravel drive, those topiary peacocks, the missing head.

Edward: This is Doctor Rogers' house!
Nugent: Yes. We can trust him.

Nugent urgently raps on the door. A dog barks.

Nugent: Strange. I didn't know he had a dog.

Female Narrator: Now, finding one transvestite on your doorstep is perhaps unfortunate. Finding two smacks of carelessness. Something wasn't right. In fact, several things weren't right. Rogers opened the door...

*[Okay, folks - time out. We promised you that you were going to really have to use your imagination - this is one of those times. Fact is, the next few seconds would probably have been confusing even with subtitles and instant video replay, but add to that the combination of shock and panic, Mr Rogers' notoriously slippy memory when it comes to names, and the fact that both Rogers and Nugent are being played tonight by the same actor, and you have a recipe for two minutes of pure chaos. So,

for this scene only, I'm playing the elderly Dr Rogers. Got it? Oh, just do your best...

The actress uses a suitable prop (glasses, wig) to adopt the demeanour of Rogers.]

Rogers: Can I help you ladies?
Nugent: Look closer. *(Nugent lifts up his hat)*
Rogers: Jack?
Nugent: Edward.
Rogers: No, I'm Peter.
Nugent: No, I know. I mean I'm Edward, Peter. Even though you sometimes call me Jack.
Rogers: Do I?
Nugent: Yes. You just did. It doesn't matter. Call me Jack if it helps.
Rogers: What would help me most right now, Jack, is knowing why you are standing on my doorstep wearing a frock and a furry hat.
Nugent: I can explain everything.
Rogers: Start with the frock.
Nugent: All right. It's a long story.
Rogers: That's fine. I'm retired.
Nugent: Can we at least come in?
Rogers: I suppose you'd better.
Nugent: Thank you.
Rogers: Well?
Nugent: Well, do you remember Edward?
Rogers: But you said that you were Edward...
Nugent: We're both Edward. You must remember Edward Jones? The man you sent to see me. The man with the bald patch that went away.
Rogers: Oh, yes, of course! With the Polaroid. That's why I know your face. But...the last time I saw you, you were a man.
*[**Edward:** So were you!
Nugent: Don't confuse them.]*
Rogers: In fact, you both were.
Nugent: We both still are. We're in disguise.
Rogers: Not, if I may venture an opinion, a very convincing one.
Nugent: Look, Peter, we haven't got time to mess around – we...

Female Narrator: *[(removing the Rogers' props)]* Nugent stopped. He thought he'd seen something. A shadow moving in the hall. He brought his finger to his lips with all the drama of a Samurai swordsman brandishing his ceremonial weapon, and the room fell deadly silent. A floorboard creaked. *(Sound effect of a floorboard creaking)* Three pairs of eyes widened. *(A similar sound effect as their eyes widen)* Someone was listening behind the door.

Tense, melodramatic music underpins the action. Nugent bravely signals Edward to get behind him, then, less bravely, to get back in front of him. Finally, after jostling for position, they arrange that Edward is to hit the light switch. The room goes black and there are some confused noises.

Nugent: Lights!

As Edward switches on the lights, Nugent is straddling the floored Sarah, pinning her down by sitting on her shoulders. Her head is hidden underneath his skirt.

Nugent: All right, you bastard – who do you work for?

A muffled reply.

Edward: Lift your frock up, Ted. Let's see his face.
Nugent: Oh. Right.

He does. A bewildered Sarah is underneath.

Nugent: Aha! Are you undercover?
Sarah: I was, until you lifted your skirt.
Edward: Are you a reporter?
Sarah: No. Who the hell are you?
Nugent: Don't tell her, Edward.
Sarah: So your name's Edward.
Edward: Oh, thanks, Ted.
Sarah: And your name's Ted.
Nugent: *(jumping off her angrily)* Brilliant! She's blown our cover.
Sarah: What cover? What the hell are you doing here?

Suddenly, we hear an angry dog, as Nugent's bum is viciously attacked by the invisible canine. Total chaos. Sarah frantically tries to calm the dog, Nugent is in agony, and Edward is dumbfounded.

Sarah: Jack! Stop it, Jack. Get down! *(She grabs him)* It's all right, Jack. I'm okay. How did you get out of your collar, eh? Excuse me.

She exits momentarily, and returns with Jack in his collar. Edward watches open-mouthed and silent. Nugent, equally dumbfounded, lies in agony clutching his bottom. There's an awkward pause.

Sarah: Okay, so I have an invisible dog.
Nugent: Oh, that's all right then. For a moment there I though something weird was going on here.
Edward: Forgive my cynicism, but I think what we're looking at here is nothing more than the sort of trick dog collar that you buy from a joke shop.
Nugent: Edward, a trick collar does not bite you on the arse.
Sarah: I'm sorry. He thought you were attacking me.
Edward: He was right.
Nugent: Oh, my God - blood!

Nugent faints.

Edward: Oh, terrific. Here we go again.

Edward gets down to try and revive him.

*[**Female Narrator:** Nugent passed out. Bad luck for him. Good luck for us. Because it means that, for the moment at least, we now only have three speaking parts to worry about. So, just for the next few minutes, I'll be Sarah...
Male Narrator: *(getting up)* I'll be Rogers, and ...
Female Narrator: *(urgent stage whisper)* Frock off!
Male Narrator: What?
Female Narrator: Take your frock off!
Male Narrator: *(realizing he's still wearing female clothing)* Shit!

He dives off and quickly changes.

Female Narrator: So, as I was saying. Just for the next few minutes, I'll be playing Sarah...

Enter Male Narrator hurriedly, now in trousers.

Male Narrator: I'll be playing Rogers, and...er...Nugent will be played by...

They look around in desperation. Finally, an unconvincing Guy Fawkes style dummy is tossed from the wings to Edward, who thrusts it down where Nugent was originally sitting.]

Rogers: Is he all right?
Edward: He's just fainted. Can't stand the sight of blood.
Rogers: Oh, dear. Put his head between his legs.

*[*Edward removes the dummy's head and places it between the dummy's legs.*]**

Edward: Give him a few minutes.
Rogers: Well, you two - I think some explanations are in order. So, shall we start with the pink trouser suit, or the invisible dog?

Female Narrator: It was going to be a long night.

*Music link. Lights fade. As they fade back up, Sarah, Edward, Rogers *[and the dummy/Nugent]* are sat down. Rogers is handing out drinks.*

Edward: Fruit flies?
Sarah: Yes. You see it's no good doing tests on something like a dog, or a cat, because it lives too long. You'd have to wait around years to see if the experiment had had any effect.
Rogers: Ah!
Sarah: Whereas fruit flies have such a short natural lifespan...
Rogers: ...that they're ideal for testing different methodologies to see which gives the best results.
Sarah: Precisely.
Rogers: Ingenious.
Sarah: My early experiments were really promising. I'd managed to get them to live to the human equivalent of about 500 years old.
Rogers: Good Lord - what's that?
Sarah: About a month.
Rogers: Oh. Still impressive though.
Edward: How?
Sarah: By making them pass through a fluctuating magnetic field in order to reach their food - my own recipe - a genetically modified extract of over-ripe bananas.
Rogers: That's very exciting.
Sarah: The pharmaceutical companies certainly thought so. They started pushing to start human trials. And then...
Edward: And then?

Sinister music underpins her reply.

Sarah: And then, one day, without warning, one of the fruit flies suddenly swelled up to the size of a tennis ball and ...exploded - into a mist of yellow sticky vapour.
Edward: Uggh!
Rogers: Good Lord. Dead?
Sarah: Er...yes. Very much so. Closely followed by all the rest. They just kept swelling up and...popping off. Something had made them become unstable.

Rogers: What?

Sarah: Who knows? I couldn't really do a post mortem - all the evidence resided on a kitchen towel. The human trials were postponed.

Edward: Oh, shame.

Sarah: I didn't give up, of course. First I made some radical adjustments to the food formula.

Rogers: And?

Sarah: And my dog became invisible. Don't ask me how - I've never been able to repeat the conditions. All I know is he scoffed all the banana extract and...vanished.

Edward: So, what happens if humans eat it?

Sarah: It just makes them fat - trust me. So then I tried something else. I increased the strength of magnetic field, reversed the polarity, and applied a strong intermittent static charge.

Edward: And?

Sarah: My house exploded.

Rogers: That's fascinating. What do you make of it, Jack - you haven't said much yet?

[Rogers looks at the dummy, then realizes after prompts from the others that he needs to swap places with the dummy to answer as Nugent - so he does.]

Nugent: More fascinating than you realize. I too have experimented with static charges. Have I not, Edward?

Edward: Yes.

Sarah: Why?

Nugent: To try and mimic the effect of lightning. You see, Edward also has a little secret, don't you, Edward.

Edward: Hardly a secret any more.

Sarah: Well, come on - we're intrigued.

Edward: Haven't you seen a newspaper?

Sarah: No.

Edward: Television?

Sarah: My television was in my house.

Edward: Oh. Right.

Nugent: He was struck by lightning five years ago. As you can see, he survived. More than survived, actually. Ever since then, he's been... how can I put this?

Edward: Straightforwardly.

Nugent: He's been getting younger. His whole metabolism has gone into reverse.

Male Narrator: Now, that's not the sort of statement you make every day, so it was interesting to note the different reactions. *[Pointing to the dummy]* Rogers, as you can see, was dumbfounded, which is pretty much what you'd expect. But Sarah, now, that was weird. No look of surprise, no questioning of the facts - just a private, enigmatic smile.

Edward: Did you hear what he said?
Sarah: Yes.
Edward: I'm getting younger.
Sarah: Yes.
Edward: Instead of older.
Sarah: Yes.
Edward: That sort of makes me...unique, in a sort of earth-shatteringly unique never before on this planet sort of way.
Sarah: Yes. Yes it does.
Edward: Have you always been this excitable?
Sarah: I knew you'd come.
Edward: What do you mean?

Sarah's smile broadens, and she gets up.

Sarah: Oh, nothing.
Nugent: You knew who'd come?
Sarah: Never mind. You know, my early experiments to increase the life of fruit flies were all based on static charges - mini lightning strikes, if you like - I was convinced it was the key to increasing their life expectancy.
Nugent: And?
Sarah: Well, unfortunately, I had to stop the experiments.
Nugent: Why?
Sarah: The data proved...disappointing.
Nugent: In what sense?
Sarah: In the sense that every fly I tested died instantly.
Edward: Terrific.
Sarah: I still passionately believed in the theory - but, well, from a scientific point of view, as you can imagine, when the fly died, it made it much harder to determine how much its life might have been extended...had it lived.

The other two take a puzzled moment to think that through.

Nugent: Peter - you've been quiet lately - what do you think?

The lights cut to a spotlight on the Female Narrator.

Female Narrator: The Rogers' household had never seen so much activity. And as night fell, and the outside world waited anxiously for news of Edward Jones, three men, a woman and an invisible dog sat exhausted, exhilarated and confused.

Meanwhile, across the globe, Edward's story was breaking in the most spectacular fashion.

Dramatic news theme - fade up lights on two presenters at desk.

Male American Newsreader: NBC News at six o'clock - I'm Dick O'Brien.
Female American Newsreader: And I'm Stacey Gonnerill.
Male American Newsreader: And I'm Dick O'Brien. The whereabouts of Edward Jones, the extraordinary British man who's growing younger instead of older, is still no clearer tonight, despite the efforts of one of the biggest multinational search parties in history. British police are looking for a blue Ford car that they believe might have been stolen by Jones as he fled his house last Friday.
Female American Newsreader: But not surprisingly, news that it might be possible to reach forty and then start growing younger is going down pretty big here in California. Forget Botox and liposuction - the latest and most extreme form of cosmetic surgery is called pyloning.
Male American Newsreader: In the Beverly Hills area alone, the LAPD has reported hundreds of cases of huge-breasted women with distended lips strapping themselves to electricity pylons and praying for an electrical storm. It's a dangerous game – especially if you get what you wished for, as our reporter Kirsty O'Donnegan now reports.
Female Reporter: Thank you, Dick. Yes, as you say, it's called pyloning, the craze of strapping yourself to a pylon and waiting for an electrical storm - some believe it can knock years off you - but it can do a lot more than that, and it's already ended in one tragedy here at Beverly Hills. Beauty Pageant Queen Sabrina Estevez last night became the first casualty of this extreme surgery, when, quite literally, she had her tits blown off. She was found to be dead on arrival at hospital. Worse still, she was back to a 32B. One of her implants was later found to have partially melted onto a cow below, who now proudly wears it like a bobble hat. Back to you, Dick.
Male American Newsreader: Thanks, Kirsty. Meanwhile, ruthless Japanese Real Estate Tycoon Ngoto Sakyoto has reportedly offered a 500 million dollar reward for the first person to track down Edward Jones and successfully extract his DNA. More on that after this short break.

News theme. Lights fade on desk.

Female Narrator: Meanwhile, the media continued to crawl all over the Jones' household like ants on jam. Three days had passed, with no sign of Edward or his mysterious doctor friend. The strain and the embarrassment of facing the whispering neighbours was all too much for Mrs Jones, who wasted no time in filing for divorce. It was, in fact, the first time in years that she'd taken an active interest in her husband.

Exit Female Narrator. We see Edward in the background, walking the 'dog'. The Male Narrator takes up the story.

Male Narrator: But what about Edward Jones himself? Well, in truth, it was all getting a bit much. He hadn't slept properly for what seemed like weeks - and he was starting to look dreadful. Getting younger was putting years on him. In short, he was tired. Dog tired. *(Staring at the empty dog collar)* In fact, he was even more tired than the dog, who didn't look tired at all.

Exit Male Narrator.

Edward: Come on, Jack - let's get you back home.

Music link. Edward walks the dog back to a waiting Sarah.

Sarah: Thanks for doing that.
Edward: No problem. I needed the air.
Sarah: Did he behave himself?
Edward: I don't know - how can you tell?
Sarah: He didn't tug on the lead or anything?
Edward: No. Hardly knew he was in there.
Sarah: Good boy, Jack!
Edward: Tell me - are his poos invisible as well?
Sarah: Course they are.
Edward: So, how can you tell if you've trodden in one?
Sarah: The usual way.
Edward: Oh. *(He sniffs at his shoe)*

They sit down on a bench.

Sarah: It's a lovely evening.
Edward: Yes.
Sarah: You look tired.
Edward: Mmm. I find I need more sleep, the younger I get.
Sarah: This business of your metabolism. Of getting younger. How does it make you feel?
Edward: Scared. I've asked Nugent to try and reverse it.
Sarah: Reverse it? You can't!
Edward: No, not yet, but he's working on it.
Sarah: No, I mean you can't! It's the most fantastic adventure of all time. Why would you want to try and deny it?
Edward: Perhaps I just want to be normal.

Sarah: Oh, no. Think it through, Edward.
Edward: I've thought it through.
Sarah: Think it through again.
Edward: I've thought it through again. And again. And again. I'm fed up with thinking it though. I just want to be me.
Sarah: What does that mean?
Edward: I just want to be an ordinary bloke, like I was before. I just want to watch telly, and read the paper, and go to the pub, and...mend pylons and...eat ham sandwiches on Fridays, and...have tie clips for my birthday, and... *(he fizzles out, depressed)*
Sarah: No you don't.
Edward: No I don't. But I don't want this either. I don't know what I want any more.
Sarah: Edward, you're at the start of an incredible journey.
Edward: Yeah, well, perhaps I don't like travelling alone.
Sarah: Edward...
Edward: Mmm?
Sarah: I want to tell you something.
Edward: Go on then.
Sarah: It's pretty...mind boggling.
Edward: What the hell. My mind's already boggled.
Sarah: But sort of...exciting too.
Edward: What?
Sarah: Don't you think it's weird that...well, think about what happened to you, and my experiments, and my house exploding, and the fact that we met like this, and, well...it can't all be just coincidence, can it?
Edward: I don't know. Can it?

A pause.

Sarah: Edward, I'm a girl who's spent a lot of time with fruit flies.
Edward: What's that supposed to mean?
Sarah: I get lonely.
Edward: Are you flirting with me?
Sarah: I'm sorry.
Edward: Don't be. I didn't say I minded.
Sarah: I'm embarrassed now.
Edward: I get lonely too.
Sarah: Do you?
Edward: Oh, God yes.
Sarah: Good.
Edward: Thanks.
Sarah: No, I just meant, it's good I'm not the only one getting lonely. It would be quite

lonely getting lonely on your own.

Edward: Earlier on - in there - you said something odd.

Sarah: I say a lot of odd things.

Edward: You said "I knew you'd come". What did you mean?

Sarah: Look! A shooting star.

Edward: Wow.

Sarah: Did you make a wish?

Edward: Erm…I have now.

Sarah: Me too.

Edward: What was yours?

Sarah: Secret. What was yours?

Edward: Secret.

Sarah: Good. That means they'll come true.

Edward: We'll see.

Sarah: You know, I wouldn't do anything to a fruit fly that I wouldn't do to myself.

Edward: What do you mean?

Sarah: There isn't a single one of my longevity experiments that I haven't tried on myself first.

Edward: You mean you've eaten that banana stuff?

Sarah: By the bucket-load. And slept in magnetic fields, and subjected myself to static charges.

Edward: Was it worth it?

Sarah: I hoped one day it might be.

Edward: Sounds dodgy to me.

Sarah: I'm used to it. I've been doing stuff like this for over eighty years.

Edward: Nevertheless you want to be careful you don't…what did you say?

Sarah: I started experimenting when I was a kid.

Edward: You said eighty years.

Sarah: Not all my experiments end in disaster, Edward. It's my birthday next month. I'll be eighty-seven years old.

Edward: My God.

Sarah: So you see, us meeting like this, well, I think there's more to it than just luck, don't you?

Edward: Are you…you're not lying to me?

Sarah: Edward, if a woman wanted to lie about her age, she wouldn't claim to be eighty-seven.

Edward: But, how do you feel…inside?

Sarah: Right now? *(She takes his hand)* Like a teenager. So I was wondering…if you did decide to go on this incredible journey of yours after all, could I possibly hitch a lift?

They edge together as if to kiss. Sarah closes her eyes, but Edward stops short, with a strange expression.

Edward: What about a wee?
Sarah: Sorry?
Edward: The dog's wee. Is that invisible as well?
Sarah: Yes.
Edward: But it's still wet and warm?
Sarah: Yes, why? Oh, bloody hell. I'm so sorry. Jack, you monster - go away. Sorry, I
think he's just jealous. He's used to being the centre of attention.

Sarah starts frantically drying Edward's leg with a tissue. Nugent enters.

Nugent: Not interrupting anything am I?
Edward: You might have been, if the dog hadn't got in first.
Nugent: Just been watching the BBC News. You'll be glad to know the world's gone
completely mad. Religious leaders are running around like headless chickens claiming
you're the devil incarnate, the FBI have just put you on the top of their most wanted
list, and a Japanese businessman has just offered a $500 million reward for the first
person to extract your DNA.
Edward: Really - and who won the snooker?
Nugent: *(angrily)* You're not taking this seriously, Edward!
Edward: *(now equally angry)* I'm taking this deadly seriously. And my DNA's
staying right where it is, thanks.
Nugent: *(backing off, slightly embarrassed)* Oh, and er…one more thing. Your wife's
divorcing you.
Edward: *(taken aback)* What?
Nugent: It was on the news.
Edward: *(clearly shaken)* Oh. Right. Looks like I'm the last to know, then.

He turns away and takes a private moment.

Sarah: I'm sorry Edward.
Edward: Are you? *(She shakes her head)* Oh, well. Probably for the best. There's only
so many tie clips a man can take.

There's a menacing rumble of thunder. They look to the skies.

Sarah: That's odd. It was fine a minute ago.
Nugent: *(producing a bunch of keys)* Come on. Rogers has lent me his car. We need to
get back to my lab straight away.
Edward: Why?
Nugent: I've been thinking it through, Edward. It took a huge shock to the system to

start this. I'm convinced the only way to stop it is another shock of equal magnitude. So, here's what we're going to do. We're going to reproduce exactly the conditions on the day you were struck by lightning.

Edward: No thanks.

Nugent: Now, as long as you're not earthed, I reckon I can stick a hundred thousand volts through your spine and you'll survive.

Edward: Some other time.

Nugent: I know it sounds scary, and it will probably blow your eyebrows off, but it's the only way.

Edward: No.

Nugent: And we're going to leave nothing to chance. I'll create an electrical field around you to mimic the effect of the pylon.

Edward: No.

Nugent: I'll match the temperature and humidity in the lab to the day you were hit.

Edward: No.

Nugent: And - even though I'm fairly certain it won't have a direct bearing, just to play safe...

Edward: No.

Nugent: ...I want you to be eating a ham sandwich.

Edward: Ted, no!

Nugent: Listen to me, Edward. It's not just the paparazzi now - it's the FBI, private detectives, pharmaceutical companies, religious nuts, ruthless bounty hunters, rich Japanese loonies - it's only a matter of time before one of them hunts you down.

Sarah: He's right, Edward. They'd never leave us alone.

Nugent: We need to reverse this before the vultures descend and tear you to shreds. Let's cure you now, and send them away empty-handed. It's the only way to make them stop.

Edward looks at Sarah, then back to Nugent.

Edward: I don't want to be cured.

Nugent: What? But you...

Edward: I've changed my mind.

Sarah offers a private smile.

Nugent: Edward, we talked about this...

Edward: I know. But things have changed.

Nugent: What things?

Edward: I'm not going to be alone any more.

He grabs Sarah's hand.

Nugent: What's going on?
Edward: It's a long story.
Sarah: Over eighty years long.

We hear a police siren, and the storm is still building.

Nugent: My God, they're on to us already. Come on.
Edward: No, you go.
Nugent: Edward, you don't know what you're letting yourself in for.
Edward: I don't care. We'll get through it together. Go on - you go, we'll be fine.
Nugent: But...I can't just leave you. Not now.
Edward: Ted, this is what I want. I know that now. I didn't before. But I do now.
Nugent: *(he sighs and turns to Sarah)* You do realize, young lady, that you've got someone very special here, don't you?
Sarah: Oh, yes. Yes. I do.
Nugent: Well, just...erm...just look after him for me.
Sarah: I will. *(Leaning forward and whispering in his ear)* And don't worry, I'll never tell anyone what I saw up your skirt.
Nugent: Cheeky.

Another thunderclap and sirens.

Edward: Go on, you don't want to be caught up in all of this. It's me they're after.

Nugent, accepting that Edward is not going to change his mind, shakes his hand.

Nugent: Good luck. You'll need it.

Nugent exits.

Edward: You're good at all this mystical stuff - is it bad luck to talk about a wish after it's come true?
Sarah: I don't think so.
Edward: Because mine has.
Sarah: Mine too.
Edward: You realize we're going to be more famous than the Beckhams.
Sarah: Yes, but hopefully with a longer shelf life.
Edward: And less tattoos.
Sarah: Don't be so sure about that.

She lifts up a garment to reveal a tattoo - a heart and two names.

Edward: "Sarah...Edward." How the bloody hell...you are a witch!

Sarah: Not really. Just a drunken moment with an old boyfriend, years and years ago. He broke my heart. It has made me rather picky about my relationships since though. They have to be tall, dark, handsome...

Edward: And called Edward.

Sarah: Precisely. You see? I knew you'd come.

Edward: You are one weird and wonderful lady.

Sarah: And so are you.

Edward: You should see me in my bikini.

Sarah: *(turning to him and taking both hands)* So, are you ready?

Edward: What for?

Sarah: For the incredible journey of life.

Edward: Let's see... *(he lifts her hands and checks her over)* Yep. All packed.

Sarah: Give us a kiss, then.

Edward: No way. You're old enough to be my mother.

Sarah: Don't knock it. One day I might have to be.

They go to kiss, but suddenly and dramatically Sarah is wracked with pain. Huge, ominous music underpins the scene.

Sarah: Arrgh!

Edward: What is it?

Sarah: I don't know, nothing - just stomach cramps, I...arrgh!

Edward: Sarah? What's wrong?

Sarah collapses back onto the bench. Suddenly, her stomach begins swelling like a gigantic inflating balloon. She is screaming. Edward is horrified but helpless.

Sarah: Help me!

Edward: What can I do? Tell me what to do!

Sarah: *(fighting through the pain)* I'm sorry Edward. I don't think...I'm going to be able to go with you after all.

Edward: No...you can't do this to me. You can't leave me on my own. I can't go through this without you. Do you hear me? Sarah! Sarah!!

Sarah: Look after Jack for me, will you?

Sarah reaches out to touch him. Her balloon-like stomach finally explodes. She slumps lifelessly to the floor.

Edward: *(quietly)* Sarah? Sarah?

A Flying Ducks Publication

Finally realizing Sarah is beyond hope, Edward screams his anger to the skies - a huge flash of lightning and thunder crack respond instantly.

Edward: No!!!!

Enter staggers off. More thunder cracks. In an exact reprise of the opening scene, powerful music emphasizes the drama of the huge lightning storm. Edward Jones, drenched and despairing, climbs to the top of the electricity pylon. He turns to the sky, screaming "Help me! Please, help me!" Suddenly, there's an almighty crack of thunder, and an explosive lightning bolt strikes, lighting up the pylon and sending his body plummeting down. The music hits a crescendo and ends. Calm after the storm. A spotlight fades up on the Female Narrator.

Female Narrator: No-one was seriously expecting to pull Edward from the manure alive and, as the charred and stinking body was eventually unearthed, the paramedic on standby to give mouth-to-mouth was keeping his fingers crossed that it wasn't even a close call.

As the lights come up, DI Thompson, a male police detective, is crouching over Edward's body, examining it. Enter DC Jarvis – a female detective, with a notepad.

DC Jarvis: Right, sir. His name's Edward Jones. He worked for the Utilities company.
DI Thompson: What the hell was he doing up there on a night like this?
DC Jarvis: Well, whatever it was, it wasn't official. He was suspended from work last month following health problems.
DI Thompson: What sort of health problems?
DC Jarvis: Severe depression, mainly, and some delusional stuff. I spoke to his wife. Well, ex-wife - she was divorcing him. She says she hadn't able to get through to him for months. He seemed to be locked away in his own world.
DI Thompson: Anything from his doctor?
DC Jarvis: Nothing official. He refused to see his own GP, claiming she was trying to stab him in the buttocks.
DI Thompson: Do what?
DC Jarvis: He told his wife he was seeing another doctor, but she never found out who. He was also convinced he was being hounded by the paparazzi, he stole his neighbour's car, he attacked a tramp in the park while wearing his wife's clothes…
DI Thompson: In a nutshell, you're telling me he's a total fruitcake.
DC Jarvis: Don't know about fruit cake, sir - possibly a fruit fly.
DI Thompson: Fruit fly?
DC Jarvis: He once said something to his wife about being a human fruit fly…
DI Thompson: Bloody hell. What goes on in the dark recesses of the mind, eh?
DC Jarvis: I've haven't got to the best bit yet, sir. His wife also says she once caught

him - are you ready for this, sir - talking to an imaginary dog.
DI Thompson: Bloody hell.
DC Jarvis: A spaniel.
DI Thompson: How did she know it was a spaniel?
DC Jarvis: I suppose she had to take his word for it.
DI Thompson: Puts my problems into perspective, I suppose.
DC Jarvis: What problems have you got, sir?
DI Thompson: Right now, a dead body and a lot of paperwork.
DC Jarvis: Shame. Good-looking chap, too.
DI Thompson: If you say so. And not very old, by the look of him.
DC Jarvis: That's the irony of it all, sir. His wife reckons that that's what's behind all this.
DI Thompson: How do you mean?
DC Jarvis: Well, apparently, he was totally obsessed by the whole idea of growing old. It completely freaked him out. She said he went berserk when he first discovered a bald spot. Took pictures of it and everything. I've got one here his wife found.

She hands her boss a crumpled Polaroid. He screws up his eyes, moving the photograph forwards and backwards, struggling to make sense of it.

DI Thompson: What the hell's this?
DC Jarvis: His head, sir. Bald patch.
DI Thompson: Really? Must get my eyes tested. Stick it in a plastic bag.
DC Jarvis: I suppose he just became more and more agitated as he got towards the big day.
DI Thompson: Big day?
DC Jarvis: I don't think it's any coincidence he did this tonight, sir. It was his birthday tomorrow. He would have been forty.

A ripple of eerie music.

DI Thompson: Isn't life supposed to start at forty?
DC Jarvis: I'll let you know, sir.
DI Thompson: How old are you, Jarvis?
DC Jarvis: Twenty-seven, sir. Twenty-eight next week.
DI Thompson: Now you've depressed me.
DC Jarvis: Why, sir?
DI Thompson: I was twenty-seven - twenty-seven years ago.
DC Jarvis: Well, your eyes might be dodgy, sir, but at least your mind's still sharp. I couldn't have worked that out so quickly.
DI Thompson: Don't be cheeky...
DC Jarvis: Oh, excuse me, sir. My mobile.

DI Thompson: What about it?
DC Jarvis: It's ringing.
DI Thompson: Bugger. Does this mean I'm going deaf as well?
DC Jarvis: No, sir. I've got it on silent vibrate.
DI Thompson: Oh. Enjoy.

She answers it in the background while Inspector Thompson crouches over the body.
There's a mysterious tingle of music.

DI Thompson: You poor sod. What was scaring you so much, eh?

He spots something in Edward's hand. He pulls it out and sniffs at it. DC Jarvis has
finished her call and returns to his side.

DC Jarvis: What's that?
DI Thompson: Ham toasty.
DC Jarvis: No time for lunch, sir. We've been called to another incident.
DI Thompson: Where?
DC Jarvis: Grange Common. Sarah Appleby's place.
DI Thompson: Oh, what now? Neighbours reported seeing flying broomsticks again?
DC Jarvis: Something a bit more substantial this time, sir. Her house has exploded.
DI Thompson: Good God. Any casualties?
DC Jarvis: So far, just a crow. But Sarah's gone missing.
DI Thompson: All right - get moving. I'll tidy up here and meet you over there. *(She*
goes to exit, but is called back by a pensive DI Thompson) DC Jarvis?
DC Jarvis: Sir?
DI Thompson: Do you ever worry about getting old?
DC Jarvis: Can't say I've really thought about it, sir.
DI Thompson: What would scare you enough…to do this to yourself?
DC Jarvis: Dunno, sir. Certainly not a few wrinkles. *(She again goes to leave, but turns*
at the last minute, having considered the question) Actually, sir…the thing that would
probably scare me most…well, it's not the getting old, is it, sir. It's being on your own.
Not having anyone to share it with. Yeah. I think that would get to me.
DI Thompson: Mmm. Okay, go on.
DC Jarvis: Sir.

He takes a final look at the toasty, tosses it off-stage, and walks away. From the direction
of the toasty, a hungry dog barks his appreciation. Thompson turns and looks, puzzled,
shakes his head and slowly exits. A spotlight narrows onto Edward's body as eerie music
builds to a crescendo. Suddenly, Edward sits bolt upright and gasps. Lights cut instantly
to blackout. Curtain.